To my
Very Favorite
Friend –
L and J.

# The Gold of Friendship

# The Gold of Friendship

By Gail Mahan

*Illustrated by Marilyn Conklin*

HALLMARK EDITIONS

# The Gold of Friendship

Have you ever found gold?

 Was it under a shining mountain?

Was it high in a gleaming castle?

Deep in a sparkling ocean?

Have you ever found gold
just by looking in someone's heart?

Gold makes you rich.

But one kind of gold
    is worth more than all others.
It isn't the gold you can spend,
    wear, or hold...

it's the kind you find in a friend.

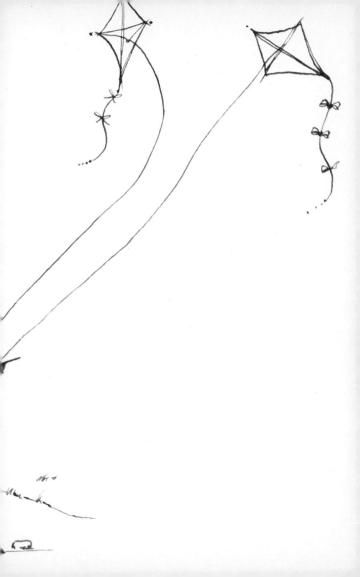

First you have to look for gold dust.
Maybe you've seen it
   on the cheeks
   of someone smiling at you.

Have you seen gold on helping hands?

On lips that say "You're dear"?

Perhaps you've seen it
on the shoes of someone coming
when you need somebody near.

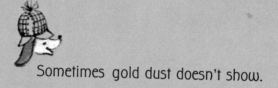

Sometimes gold dust doesn't show.

Then you have to look closer
        and dig deeper. But if you believe
        that you'll find gold inside,
        chances are you will.

If you give up too soon,
  you may miss buried treasure.

It may take time to find gold.
But it starts to shine
    when you and a friend trade
        secret secrets. . .

or dream silently together...

when you're together sharing,
      pleasing, caring,
   in sad and happy weather.

When you first see your smile
on someone else's face,
you've just discovered gold.

For a friend is the most precious
discovery of all.

And you'll know that's true,
when you know a friend
has found gold in you.